It's Raining On Your Parade, Charlie Brown

Selected cartoons from
DON'T HASSLE ME WITH YOUR
SIGHS, CHUCK Vol. 1

Charles M. Schulz

CORONET BOOKS
Hodder Fawcett, London

First published by Fawcett Publications
Inc., New York

Coronet edition 1980

Printed in Great Britain for Hodder
Fawcett Ltd., Mill Road, Dunton Green,
Sevenoaks, Kent (Editorial Office: 47
Bedford Square, London, WC1 3DP) by
C. Nicholls & Company Ltd,
The Philips Park Press, Manchester

ISBN 0 340 25398 3

Dear Truffles,
I am sorry that I haven't been to see you, but I am not sure I could find your house again.
I have a "friend" who could show me the way, but he won't.
Some "friends" turn out to be double-crossers!
SIGH
HEE HEE HEE HEE
SCHULZ

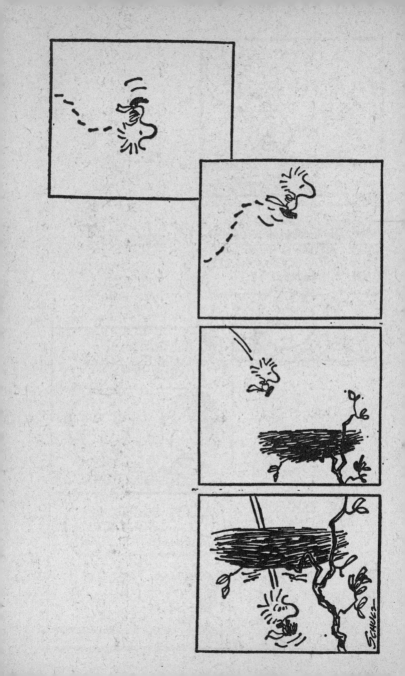

HUMOUR FROM CORONET

CHARLES M. SCHULZ

☐	10595 X	Here's To You Charlie Brown	60p
☐	10541 0	Nobody's Perfect Charlie Brown	60p
☐	10673 5	Very Funny Charlie Brown	60p
☐	12544 6	What Next Charlie Brown	60p
☐	16712 2	What Now Charlie Brown	60p
☐	18303 9	There's No-one Like You Snoopy	60p
☐	21236 5	It's All Yours Snoopy	60p
☐	21983 ⁴	You've Got To be You, Snoopy	60p

JOHNNY HART

☐	19873 1	B.C. Cave In	60p
☐	16477 8	Back to B.C.	60p
☐	18780 8	B.C. Is Alive And Well	60p
☐	20653 5	B.C. One More Time	60p

JOHNNY HART and BRANT PARKER

☐	20529 6	Long Live The King	60p
☐	18604 6	There's a Fly in My Swill	60p
☐	16476 X	The Peasants Are Revolting	60p
☐	15816 6	The King's A Fink	60p

All these books are available at your local bookshop or newsagent, or can be ordered direct from the publisher. Just tick the titles you want and fill in the form below.

Prices and availability subject to change without notice.

••

CORONET BOOKS, P.O. Box 11, Falmouth, Cornwall.
Please send cheque or postal order, and allow the following for postage and packing:

U.K. – One book 25p plus 10p per copy for each additional book ordered, up to a maximum of £1.05.

B.F.P.O. and EIRE – 25p for the first book plus 10p per copy for the next 8 books, thereafter 5p per book.

OTHER OVERSEAS CUSTOMERS – 40p for the first book and 12p per copy for each additional book.

Name ....

Address ....

....